Contents

KEY STAGE 2

Premier

Large numbers

In a number, each digit has a **place value**. Look at each digit's place to work out its value.

This number is four hundred and eighty-two thousand, one hundred and fifty-six.

hundred thousands	ten thousands	thousands	hundreds	tens	ones
4	8	2	1	5	6

When you multiply numbers by 10, 100 or 1000 all the digits move to the left and the spaces are filled with zeros.

$$285 \times 10 = 2850$$
$$285 \times 100 = 28\ 500$$

When you divide numbers by 10, 100 or 1000 all the digits are moved to the right and zeros are taken off the end.

$$17\ 000 \div 100 = 170$$
$$17\ 000 \div 1000 = 17$$

I Write these as numbers.

a thirty-two thousand and fifty ➞ _____

b four hundred and eighty thousand ➞ _____

c two hundred thousand, five hundred and twelve ➞ _____

d three thousand and seventy-six ➞ _____

e eight hundred and forty-seven thousand ➞ _____

Write these as words.

f 29 050 ➞ _____

g 415 000 ➞ _____

h 105 269 ➞ _____

II Write the numbers coming in and out of each machine.

a

IN				320	2800	9000	4852
OUT	740	3050	2000				

b

IN					48	250	4150
OUT	600	1400	67 500	225 000			

c

IN				6	14	29	345
OUT	8000	17 000	141 000				

Number sequences

Negative numbers come before zero on a number line.

←——— negative numbers ———→←——— positive numbers ———→

-8 -7 -6 -5 -4 -3 -2 -1 0 1 2 3 4 5 6 7 8

1 Write the missing numbers in these sequences.

a 28 ☐ 46 55 64 ☐ ☐

b 57 51 ☐ ☐ 33 27 ☐

c -8 ☐ -2 1 ☐ 7 ☐

d 19 ☐ 9 4 ☐ -6 ☐

e -1 -5 -9 ☐ -17 ☐ ☐

f 24 14 4 ☐ ☐ -26 ☐

g ☐ -19 -8 ☐ 14 25 ☐

h 17 7 ☐ ☐ -23 ☐ ☐

2 Write the number that each arrow points to.

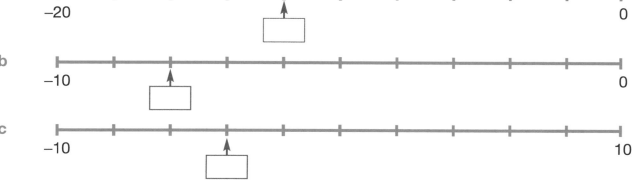

a -20 ——————↑——————— 0

b -10 ———↑————————— 0

c -10 ————↑———————— 10

d -100 —————————↑—— 0

3

Decimals

A **decimal point** separates whole numbers from decimal fractions.

24.85

2 tens (20)   4 ones (4)   8 tenths ($\frac{8}{10}$)   5 hundredths ($\frac{5}{100}$)

I Write the decimal number each arrow points to.

0   0.5   1

a [   ]   b [   ]   c [   ]   d [   ]

15   15.5   16

e [   ]   f [   ]   g [   ]   h [   ]

II Draw lines to join the matching decimals and fractions.

0.2   0.25   0.8

0.5   0.3   0.75

$\frac{1}{2}$ $\frac{3}{4}$ $\frac{3}{10}$ $\frac{1}{5}$ $\frac{1}{4}$ $\frac{4}{5}$

Quick calculations

You need to know these **facts** and recall them as quickly as possible:

- addition and subtraction facts to 20
- multiplication and division table facts to 10 × 10.

If there are brackets, always work out the brackets first.

$$30 - (4 \times 5) = \boxed{}$$
$$30 - 20 = \boxed{}$$
$$30 - 20 = 10$$

I Time yourself. How quickly can you answer each set?

a
$8 + 7 =$
$6 + 9 =$
$5 + 7 =$
$6 + 8 =$
$9 + 9 =$
$8 + 3 =$
$7 + 6 =$
$8 + 8 =$
$4 + 9 =$
$9 + 7 =$

b
$15 - 9 =$
$13 - 7 =$
$12 - 8 =$
$14 - 6 =$
$13 - 6 =$
$12 - 5 =$
$18 - 9 =$
$17 - 8 =$
$11 - 7 =$
$16 - 8 =$

c
$5 \times 7 =$
$9 \times 9 =$
$8 \times 5 =$
$4 \times 6 =$
$7 \times 7 =$
$9 \times 6 =$
$7 \times 3 =$
$4 \times 8 =$
$9 \times 5 =$
$8 \times 8 =$

d
$56 \div 7 =$
$40 \div 8 =$
$63 \div 9 =$
$24 \div 4 =$
$49 \div 7 =$
$27 \div 9 =$
$32 \div 8 =$
$48 \div 6 =$
$81 \div 9 =$
$54 \div 6 =$

I Answer these and use the code to find the name of the 'King of the Tissues!'

a $(7 \times 5) + 4 =$

b $60 - (8 \times 6) =$

c $(5 \times 5) - 10 =$

d $15 + (32 \div 8) =$

e $(7 + 13) \times 3 =$

f $24 + (18 \div 3) =$

g $(11 - 4) \times 7 =$

h $(17 - 9) \times 10 =$

i $3 + (6 \times 6) =$

j $(72 \div 8) + 5 =$

k $60 - (6 \times 5) =$

l $(63 \div 9) + 9 =$

CODE
80 = C
30 = E
12 = A
15 = N
49 = R
14 = I
19 = D
39 = H
60 = K
16 = F

His name is King

Triangles

Learn the names of different types of triangle.

Equilateral triangle	Right-angled triangle	Isosceles triangle	Scalene triangle
3 equal sides and 3 equal angles	1 right angle	2 equal sides 2 equal angles	No sides the same length

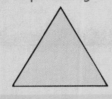  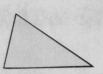

I Colour each triangle to match the key. Use a ruler to help you decide.

Key:

equilateral

isosceles

scalene

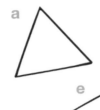  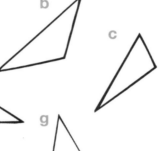 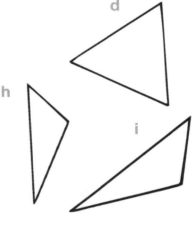

a   b   c   d   e   f   g   h   i

II Write the letter of each triangle in the correct place on the Venn diagram.

a   e

b   f

c   g

d   h

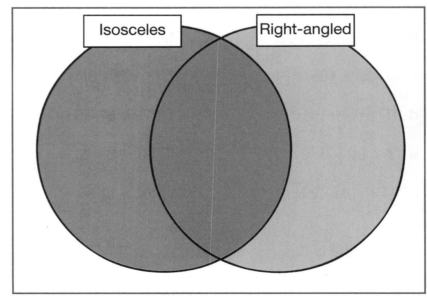

Isosceles   Right-angled

Comparing and ordering numbers

When you put decimals **in order**, it may help to write them under each other. Make sure you line up the decimal points.

For example:

7.45   7.04   7.6   70.5   → 7 . 0 4
7 . 4 5
Compare each of the columns.   7 . 6
70 . 5

The < and > sign are used to compare numbers.

> means **is greater than**

5.6 > 5.52

< means **is less than**

8.31 < 8.42

I This chart shows the height and weight of a group of men.

	Alan	Mark	Salif	Jim	Ali	Steve
Height (m)	1.71	1.62	1.65	1.79	1.7	1.82
Weight (kg)	74.3	80.2	79.8	87.3	70.6	87.1

a Write the heights in order, starting with the tallest.

☐ ☐ ☐ ☐ ☐ ☐

b Write the weights in order, starting with the heaviest.

☐ ☐ ☐ ☐ ☐ ☐

I Write the missing > or < signs on these decimal chains.

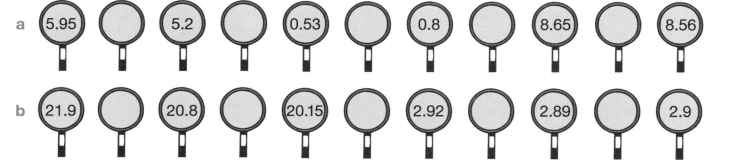

a (5.95) ( ) (5.2) ( ) (0.53) ( ) (0.8) ( ) (8.65) ( ) (8.56)

b (21.9) ( ) (20.8) ( ) (20.15) ( ) (2.92) ( ) (2.89) ( ) (2.9)

Time

Timetables and digital watches often use the **24-hour clock** time.

6.30am → 06:30   6.30pm → 18:30

I **Write these as 24-hour clock times.**

a 7.30am → [   ]

b 9.00pm → [   ]

c 10.15am → [   ]

d 4.45pm → [   ]

e 2.10am → [   ]

f 11.50pm → [   ]

Write these times using am and pm.

g 09:30 → [   ]

h 15:00 → [   ]

i 20:15 → [   ]

j 13:40 → [   ]

k 10:55 → [   ]

l 22:20 → [   ]

II **Answer these questions about the train timetable.**

a How many minutes is each journey from Gradbury to Stainton?

_____

b Which is the first train you could catch from Gradbury to arrive in Malford in the afternoon?

_____

c How many minutes does the 12:28 from Stainton take to arrive in Selbourn?

_____

d If you arrive at Gradbury station at 5.25pm, how long do you need to wait for the next train to Selbourn?

_____

TIMETABLE				
Station	**Times**			
Gradbury	09:40	11:55	14:05	17:46
Stainton	10:13	12:28	14:38	18:19
Malford	10:29	12:50	15:00	18:37
Selbourn	11:04	13:25	15:38	19:11

Fractions

There are **two numbers** that show a fraction:

$$\frac{2 \rightarrow \text{numerator}}{3 \rightarrow \text{denominator}}$$

The **denominator** shows the number of equal parts.

The **numerator** shows how many of the equal parts are used.

Equivalent fractions are worth the same.

$$\frac{2}{3} = \frac{4}{6} = \frac{8}{12}$$

We usually write fractions using the smallest possible denominator.

---

1 Complete the equivalent fractions.

a  $\frac{\square}{10} = \frac{\square}{5}$

b $\frac{\square}{12} = \frac{\square}{3}$

c $\frac{\square}{8} = \frac{\square}{4}$

d $\frac{\square}{15} = \frac{\square}{5}$

e $\frac{8}{12} = \frac{\square}{3}$

f $\frac{\square}{18} = \frac{1}{2}$

g $\frac{4}{20} = \frac{1}{\square}$

h $\frac{20}{50} = \frac{2}{\square}$

i $\frac{\square}{20} = \frac{9}{10}$

j $\frac{18}{24} = \frac{3}{\square}$

---

2 Write these fractions in order, starting with the smallest. Use the wall to help you.

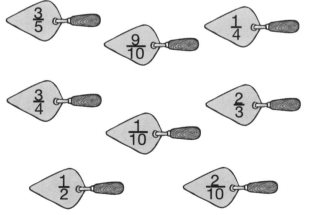

Smallest   Largest

Measures

It is helpful to learn the start (or prefix) of some **measuring words.**

Start of word →	deci	centi	milli	kilo
Number link →	$\frac{1}{10}$	$\frac{1}{100}$	$\frac{1}{1000}$	1000

1 kg 400 g = 1.4 kg

2 l 300 ml = 2.3 l

4 m 50 cm = 4.5 m

I **Write these lengths.**

a $3\frac{1}{2}$ km = ☐ m

b 40 mm = ☐ cm

c 150 cm = ☐ m

d 8 cm = ☐ mm

e $\frac{1}{4}$ m = ☐ cm

f 6500 m = ☐ km

g 22 cm = ☐ mm

h 18 km = ☐ m

i $4\frac{3}{4}$ m = ☐ cm

j 65 mm = ☐ cm

II **Write each weight shown on these scales.**

a

☐ kg

b

☐ kg

c

☐ kg

d

☐ kg

e

☐ kg

f

☐ kg

Addition

When you add numbers, decide whether to use a **mental method** or a **written method**.

Mental method

160 + 59

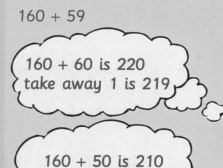

160 + 60 is 220
take away 1 is 219

160 + 50 is 210
210 + 9 is 219

Written method

4365 + 3718

```
    4365
+   3718
_____
    8083
    1   1
```

Start with the ones and add each column. Don't forget to 'carry over' any tens, hundreds or thousands.

Use the numbers from the grid to answer these.

a Which two numbers total 140? ☐ and ☐

b What is the sum of the two largest numbers? ☐

c What is the total of the three smallest numbers? ☐

d What is the sum of the four corner numbers? ☐

e Which two numbers add up to 210? ☐ and ☐

f What is the sum of the numbers in the top row? ☐

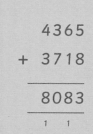

75	290	54
250	165	86
38	124	62

Use the written or mental method to answer these.

a 5094
+ 3168
_____

b 3629
+ 8294
_____

c 4816
+ 1247
_____

d 1498
+ 7527
_____

e £17.90
+ £28.54
_____

f £87.91
+ £48.14
_____

g £35.29
+ £13.46
_____

h £38.54
+ £27.86
_____

Area and perimeter

The **area** of a rectangle = length × width

The **perimeter** is the distance around the edge.

Some shapes can be broken into rectangles.

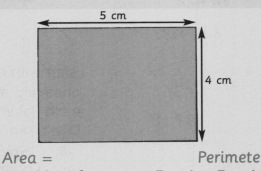

Area = 5 × 4 = 20 cm²

Perimeter = 5 + 4 + 5 + 4 = 18 cm

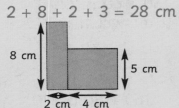

Area = (4 × 5) + (2 × 8) = 20 + 16 = 36 cm²

Perimeter = 4 + 5 + 4 + 2 + 8 + 2 + 3 = 28 cm

I Work out the area and perimeter of each shape.

a perimeter = ☐ cm
  area = ☐ cm²

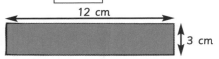

c perimeter = ☐ cm
  area = ☐ cm²

d perimeter = ☐ cm
  area = ☐ cm²

b perimeter = ☐ cm
  area = ☐ cm²

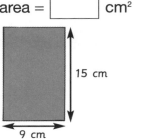

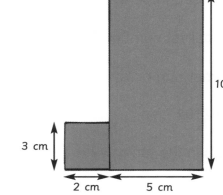

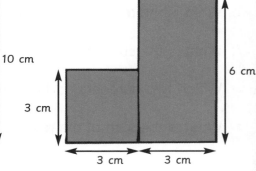

II Answer these problems.

a The perimeter of a square is 36 cm. What is its area?

☐ cm²

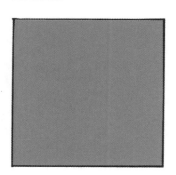

b A rectangle has an area of 18 cm². Each side is an exact number of cm. What could the perimeter be in cm?

☐ cm

or

☐ cm

or

☐ cm

c The area of a square is 64 cm². What is its perimeter?

☐ cm

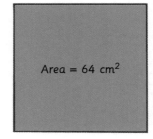

Area = 64 cm²

Prisms and pyramids

The shape of the ends of a **prism** give it its name.

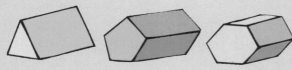

triangular prism   pentagonal prism   hexagonal prism

The shape of the base gives a **pyramid** its name.

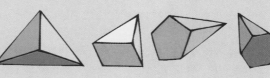

tetrahedron   square-based pyramid   pentagonal-based pyramid   hexagonal-based pyramid

Cubes and cuboids are special types of prism, because every face is a square or rectangle.

The tetrahedron is a special type of pyramid, because each of the 4 faces is a triangle.

I Tick the correct box for each shape.

     Prisms   Pyramids

a ☐ ☐
b ☐ ☐
c ☐ ☐
d ☐ ☐
e ☐ ☐
f ☐ ☐
g ☐ ☐
h ☐ ☐

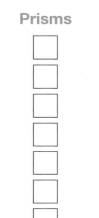
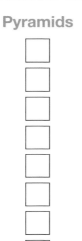
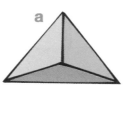
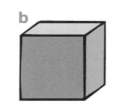

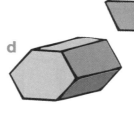
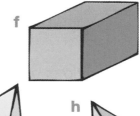
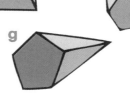

II Draw a line to join each shape to the correct number of faces, edges and vertices.

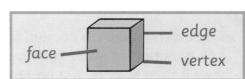

face   edge   vertex

5 faces
8 edges
5 vertices

4 faces
6 edges
4 vertices

6 faces
12 edges
8 vertices

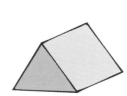

5 faces
9 edges
6 vertices

13

Ratio

Ratios are used to compare two quantities.

'... to every ...' '... for every ...' '... in every ...' are used to describe ratios.

For every 3 red stars there is 1 yellow star.
The ratio is 1 to 3.

The ratio is still 1 yellow star to every 3 red stars.

I Colour these tile patterns.

a The ratio of red to blue is 1 to every 2.

b The ratio of green to yellow is 2 to every 3.

c The ratio of red to yellow is 3 to every 5.

II Answer these.

a A chicken must be cooked for
45 minutes for every kg. How long
will it take to cook a 2 kg chicken? _____

b $\frac{1}{2}$ teaspoon of salt is required for each 500 g of flour.
How much salt is needed for $1\frac{1}{2}$ kg flour? _____

c The juice of $\frac{1}{2}$ lemon is needed for each litre of sauce.
How many lemons are needed for 3 litres? _____

d In a pie, 6 cherries are added for each plum.
How many plums are needed for 24 cherries? _____

e For each 25 g of raisins, 50 g of sultanas are needed.
How many sultanas are needed for 50 g of raisins? _____

Subtraction

If you cannot **subtract** numbers mentally, use a written method. Look at these two methods for 734 − 278.

Number line method

2 + 20 + 434 = 456

278 onto 280 is 2. 280 onto 300 is 20. 300 onto 734 is 434.

Column method

```
  12 1
 6 7 8 4
 - 2 7 8
 _____
   4 5 6
```

- Start with the ones column, taking away the bottom number from the top.
- If the top number is smaller than the bottom, exchange a ten, or a hundred.

I Choose a method to answer these.

a Find the difference between 184 and 367.

b What is 253 subtract 176?

c What is 852 take away 483?

d Decrease 813 by 125.

e Subtract 218 from 1186.

f What is the difference between 2084 and 2257?

g What is 1437 minus 1185?

h What number is 2425 less than 3812?

II Write the digits 2 to 9 on small squares of paper. Arrange them on these squares as subtractions so you can answer these.

a What is the biggest answer you can make?   =

b What is the smallest answer you can make?   =

c Give an answer as near as possible to 2000.

Square numbers

Square numbers are made when **two identical whole numbers** are multiplied together.

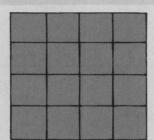

$4 \times 4 = 16$

16 is a square number.

4×4 is 4 squared.

This is written as 4^2.

$4^2 = 16$

 Answer these.

a What is 3 squared?

[ ]

What is 10 squared?

[ ]

What is 6 squared?

[ ]

What is 2 squared?

[ ]

b [ ] × [ ] = 64

[ ] × [ ] = 16

[ ] × [ ] = 25

[ ] × [ ] = 81

[ ] × [ ] = 1

[ ] × [ ] = 49

c 5^2 = [ ]

9^2 = [ ]

2^2 = [ ]

7^2 = [ ]

1^2 = [ ]

8^2 = [ ]

10^2 = [ ]

6^2 = [ ]

 Work out the lengths of each side.

a
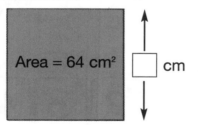
Area = 64 cm²   [ ] cm

b
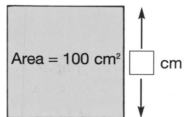
Area = 100 cm²   [ ] cm

c
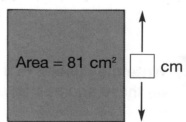
Area = 81 cm²   [ ] cm

d
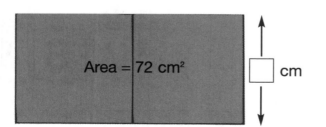
Area = 72 cm²   [ ] cm

e
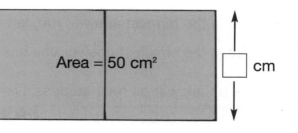
Area = 50 cm²   [ ] cm

How many vertices (corners) does a square-based pyramid have?

a 5   b 6   c 4   d 8

Answer: a

A box holds 6 pencils. If there are 40 pencils, how many boxes are needed to hold all the pencils?

a 7   b 6   c 10   d 8

Answer: a

Which of these numbers has a remainder of 3 when it is divided by 4?

a 218   b 325   c 191   d 257

Answer: c

Which of these is a multiple of 4?

a 114   b 108   c 126   d 138

Answer: b

$\frac{1}{8}$ of 400 ml is:

a 5 ml   c 50 ml

b 20 ml   d 200 ml

Answer: c

What is the size of the missing angle?

?   55°

a 45°   b 145°   c 125°   d 135°

Answer: c

What is half of 9.8 kg?

a 4.9 kg   c 4.54 kg

b 5.4 kg   d 4.8 kg

Answer: a

The area of a square is 36 cm². What is the length of each side?

a 9 cm   b 4 cm   c 8 cm   d 6 cm

Answer: d

Which of these numbers is a multiple of both 3 and 4?

a 52   b 76   c 64   d 48

Answer: d

What fraction is the same as 0.75?

a $\frac{5}{7}$　　**b** $\frac{1}{4}$　　**c** $\frac{3}{4}$　　**d** $\frac{7}{10}$

Answer: **c**

Which of these fractions is not equivalent to $\frac{2}{3}$?

a $\frac{10}{15}$　　**b** $\frac{8}{12}$　　**c** $\frac{6}{18}$　　**d** $\frac{4}{6}$

Answer: **c**

What is the missing number?

$$\boxed{} \div 8 = 8$$

a 1　　**b** 64　　**c** 16　　**d** 56

Answer: **b**

What is the difference between 88 and 103?

a 15　　**b** 25　　**c** 21　　**d** 17

Answer: **a**

What is the name for this triangle:

a equilateral triangle
b isosceles triangle
c right-angled triangle
d scalene triangle

Answer: **b**

6.45 metres is the same as:

a 64.5 cm　　**c** 645 cm
b 640 cm　　**d** 6450 cm

Answer: **c**

What is 30 multiplied by 8?

a 240　　**b** 210　　**c** 270　　**d** 2400

Answer: **a**

What is the answer to this:

$$4 + (5 \times 3) = \boxed{}$$

a 27　　**b** 12　　**c** 17　　**d** 19

Answer: **d**

What is the perimeter of this rectangle?

8 cm　　15 cm

a 46 cm　　**c** 38 cm
b 23 cm　　**d** 44 cm

Answer: **a**

Subtract 199 from 500. The answer is:

a 401 **b** 399 **c** 301 **d** 309

Answer: c

What is 18.62 km rounded to the nearest kilometre?

a 18 km **c** 10 km

b 20 km **d** 19 km

Answer: d

To make an 'Orange Fizz', half a carton of orange juice is used for every litre of lemonade. How many cartons of orange juice are needed for 6 litres of lemonade?

a 4 cartons **c** 3 cartons

b 2 cartons **d** 6 cartons

Answer: c

What is the remainder if 88 is divided by 9?

a 6 **b** 5 **c** 7 **d** 8

Answer: c

What is 10% of £5?

a 50p **b** 5p **c** 15p **d** 10p

Answer: a

A cake costs 75p. What change would there be from £5 for 3 cakes?

a £2.25 **c** £3.75

b £3.25 **d** £2.75

Answer: d

What is the area of this rectangle?

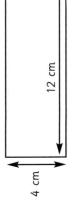

4 cm

12 cm

a 28 cm² **c** 48 cm²

b 44 cm² **d** 32 cm²

Answer: c

Which of these numbers is not a factor of 18?

a 4 **b** 6 **c** 9 **d** 2

Answer: a

What is 52 multiplied by 6?

a 312 **b** 302 **c** 412 **d** 308

Answer: a

What is the missing number?

−23   −13   [ ]   7   17   27

a −7   **b** −3   **c** 0   **d** −10

Answer: b

What is 7.45pm using 24-hour time?

a 0745   **b** 1745   **c** 1545   **d** 1945

Answer: d

What is the sum of the first four odd numbers?

a 18   **b** 15   **c** 16   **d** 20

Answer: c

What is the missing number?

104   95   86   [ ]   68   59

a 79   **b** 78   **c** 77   **d** 76

Answer: c

What is double 4.8?

a 8.8   **b** 8.6   **c** 9.2   **d** 9.6

Answer: d

What is $\frac{3}{4}$ of 12?

a 9   **b** 8   **c** 10   **d** 6

Answer: a

What is 30 less than 75?

a 105   **b** 35   **c** 55   **d** 45

Answer: d

What is the missing number?

$0.5 + [ ] + 1.3 = 2.7$

a 0.9   **b** 1.2   **c** 0.8   **d** 1.1

Answer: a

6.8 cm is the same as:

a 0.68 mm   **c** 680 mm

b 68 mm   **d** 6.8 mm

Answer: b

Factors

The factors of a number **divide exactly** into the number.

Factors can be put in order or in pairs.

Factors of 15

In order: 1, 3, 5, 15

In pairs: (1, 15) (3, 5)

I Write the factors of these numbers in order.

a **12** → _____

b **20** → _____

c **25** → _____

d **32** → _____

e **40** → _____

f **55** → _____

Write the factors of these numbers in pairs.

g **18** → _____

h **24** → _____

i **42** → _____

j **30** → _____

k **60** → _____

l **28** → _____

II Use these numbers to answer each question.

a Which number is a factor of 64? ☐

b Which number is a factor of 35? ☐

c Which number is a factor of 18? ☐

d Which two numbers are factors of 40? ☐ ☐

e Which two numbers are factors of 36? ☐ ☐

f Which two numbers are factors of 60? ☐ ☐

g True or False? 12, 8 and 9 are all factors of 72. _____

Symmetry

A **line of symmetry** divides a shape in half.

One half is the **reflection** of the other half.

Some shapes have no lines of symmetry. Others have one or more.

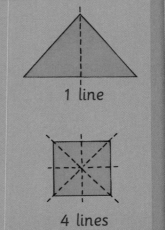

0 lines   1 line

2 lines   4 lines

I Name each quadrilateral and draw in any lines of symmetry.

a

c

e

b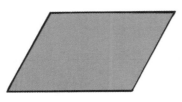

d

f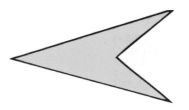

II Draw the reflection of each shape.

a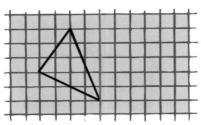

c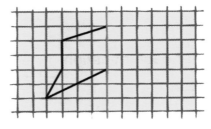

e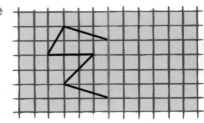

b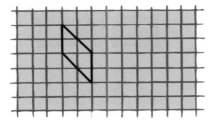

d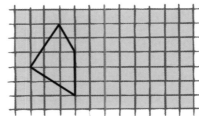

f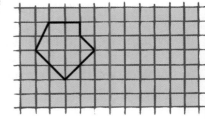

Lines

Parallel lines never meet. They always keep the same distance apart.

Perpendicular lines meet at right angles.

To measure lines accurately you may need to use millimetres (mm).

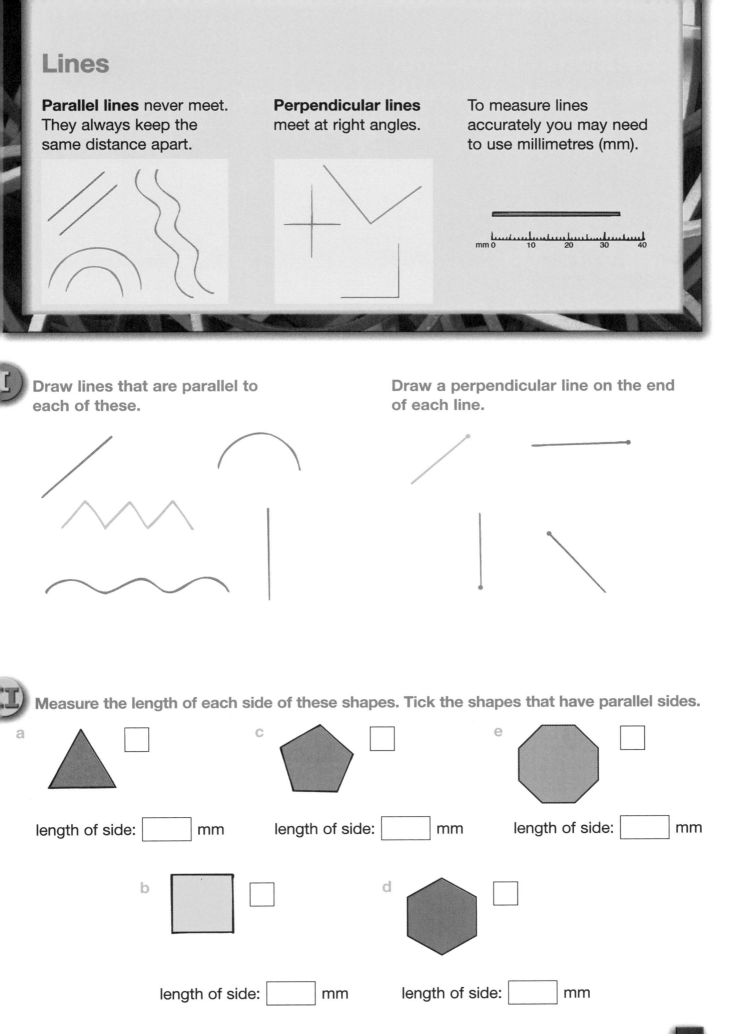

Draw lines that are parallel to each of these.

Draw a perpendicular line on the end of each line.

Measure the length of each side of these shapes. Tick the shapes that have parallel sides.

a

length of side: ☐ mm

c

length of side: ☐ mm

e

length of side: ☐ mm

b

length of side: ☐ mm

d

length of side: ☐ mm

19

Fractions of amounts

To find a fraction of an amount, divide by the **denominator**.

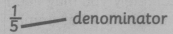 $\frac{1}{5}$ — denominator

$\frac{1}{4}$ of 12 kg = 3 kg   12 kg ÷ 4 = 3 kg

I **Answer these.**

a $\frac{1}{3}$ of £18   = £ [ ]   g $\frac{1}{100}$ of £8   = [ ] p

b $\frac{1}{4}$ of 16 cm   = [ ] cm   h $\frac{1}{4}$ of 96p   = [ ] p

c $\frac{1}{2}$ of 250 g   = [ ] g   i $\frac{1}{8}$ of 72 l   = [ ] l

d $\frac{1}{10}$ of 1500 m = [ ] m   j $\frac{1}{5}$ of 250 ml   = [ ] ml

e $\frac{1}{8}$ of 32 l   = [ ] l   k $\frac{1}{3}$ of 99p   = [ ] p

f $\frac{1}{6}$ of 36 kg   = [ ] kg   l $\frac{1}{12}$ of 60 kg   = [ ] kg

II **Draw lines to join the matching answers.**

 $\frac{1}{10}$ of 700

 $\frac{1}{4}$ of 320

 $\frac{1}{5}$ of 300

 $\frac{1}{8}$ of 560

 $\frac{1}{3}$ of 240

 $\frac{1}{6}$ of 300

 $\frac{1}{2}$ of 120

 $\frac{1}{8}$ of 400

Handling data

Data can be shown on graphs.
Graphs have **axes** and a **scale**.

Read the scale and labels on the axes carefully.

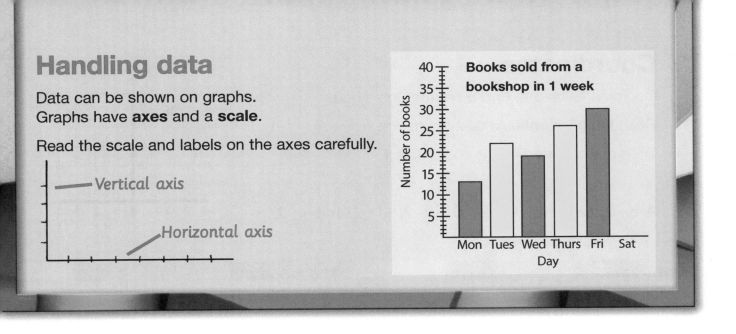

Vertical axis

Horizontal axis

Books sold from a bookshop in 1 week

Number of books

Mon Tues Wed Thurs Fri Sat

Day

---

1 Look at the graph above and answer these.

a How many books were sold on Thursday? _____

b On which day were 22 books sold? _____

c How many more books were sold on
Friday than on Monday? _____

d On which day were half the number of books
sold than on Thursday? _____

e On Saturday, the bookshop sold as many books
as the total number of books sold on Monday and
Tuesday. Show this on the graph. _____

f How many books were sold in total in the week,
including Saturday? _____

---

2 Carry out a word survey. Choose a page from one of your books. Count the number of
letters for each word and record it on this tally chart. Show your results on a bar chart.

Number of letters for each word

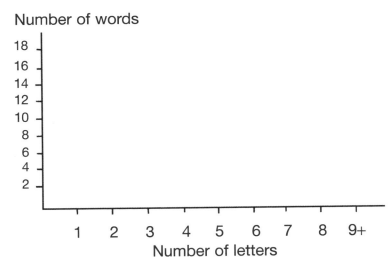

1	
2	
3	
4	
5	
6	
7	
8	
9+	

Number of words

18
16
14
12
10
8
6
4
2

1   2   3   4   5   6   7   8   9+

Number of letters

Coordinates

Coordinates help to **find a position** on a grid.

Read the **horizontal** (x) coordinate first →.

Then read the **vertical** (y) coordinate ↑.

A is (2, 6)   B is (4, 2)   C is (–2, 5)   D is (–4, 2)

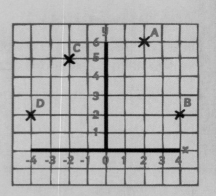

 Follow these instructions.

a   Start at (0, 0).

b   Use a ruler to draw straight lines to
join these in order:

(0, 0) → (2, 4) → (5, 5) → (1, 6) → (0, 9)

c   If **y** is a line of symmetry, complete the
symmetrical shape.

d   Write the coordinates to complete
the shape.

_____

_____

II **Write the coordinates shown.**

A → ([ ] , [ ])

B → ([ ] , [ ])

C → ([ ] , [ ])

These are three vertices
of a rectangle.

Plot the fourth vertex (D) and
draw the rectangle. Write the
final coordinates.

D → ([ ] , [ ])

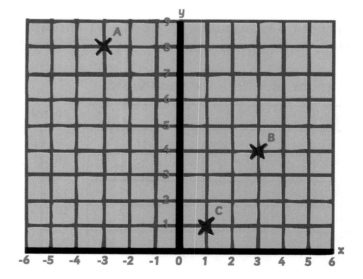

Percentages

% (per cent) shows a fraction out of 100.

$$40\% = \frac{40}{100}$$

$$25\% = \frac{25}{100}$$

% also means **percentage**.

Try to learn these percentages.

$$10\% = \frac{10}{100} = \frac{1}{10} = 0.1$$

$$25\% = \frac{25}{100} = \frac{1}{4} = 0.25$$

$$50\% = \frac{50}{100} = \frac{1}{2} = 0.5$$

1% of £1 = 1p

10% of £1 = 10p

20% of £1 = 20p

50% of £1 = 50p

I Write the percentages of each shape coloured in.

a 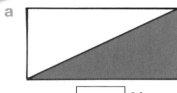 ☐ %

b  ☐ %

c 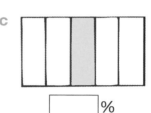 ☐ %

d 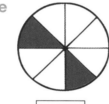 ☐ %

e  ☐ %

f  ☐ %

Answer these.

g 10% of £2 = ☐ p

h 25% of £10 = £ ☐ p

i 20% of £5 = £ ☐

j 50% of £6 = £ ☐

k 5% of £4 = ☐ p

l 75% of £2 = £ ☐ p

II These are the ingredients for a 400 g cake. Write the weight of each ingredient.

CAKE RECIPE

35% dried fruit

15% butter

30% flour

10% sugar

10% eggs and nuts

dried fruit = ☐ g

butter = ☐ g

flour = ☐ g

sugar = ☐ g

eggs and nuts = ☐ g

Rounding decimals

Decimal numbers can be **rounded** to the nearest **whole number**.

Look at the **tenths** digit.

If it is 5 or more, round up to the next whole number.

If it is less than 5, round down and the whole number stays the same.

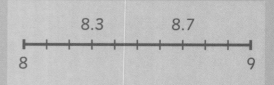

8.3   8.7

8   9

8.7 rounds **up** to 9

8.3 rounds **down** to 8

I Round each of these to the nearest whole number.

a 4.7 → ☐

b 6.4 → ☐

c 9.1 → ☐

d 12.5 → ☐

e 17.9 → ☐

f 14.3 → ☐

g 6.8 m → ☐ m

h 11.4 kg → ☐ kg

i 15.5 l → ☐ l

j 4.35 km → ☐ km

k 8.62 l → ☐ l

l 9.45 kg → ☐ kg

4.35 km

II Each of these prices rounds to either £5 or £6. Draw a line to join each label to the correct rounded amount.

 £6.09

 £5.60

 £5.00

 £5.39

£5.45

£5.56

 £6.00

£5.64

 £4.82

 £5.40

Multiples

Multiples are numbers made by **multiplying together** two other numbers.

> The first 6 multiples of 3: 3, 6, 9, **12**, 15, 18
>
> The first 6 multiples of 4: 4, 8, **12**, 16, 20, 24
>
> 12 is a **common multiple** of both 3 and 4.

Multiples go on and on: 300 is a multiple of 3 and 4000 is a multiple of 4.

Other common multiples of 3 and 4 include 60, 120 and 240.

I **Circle the correct answers.**

a The 15th multiple of 2 is:

| 25 | 30 | 36 |

e A common multiple of 3 and 5 is:

| 25 | 35 | 45 |

b The 11th multiple of 8 is:

| 80 | 96 | 88 |

f A common multiple of 2 and 3 is:

| 40 | 36 | 28 |

c The 20th multiple of 10 is:

| 20 | 200 | 2000 |

g A common multiple of 5 and 6 is:

| 70 | 80 | 90 |

d The 100th multiple of 4 is:

| 400 | 100 | 200 |

h A common multiple of 3 and 10 is:

| 100 | 120 | 160 |

II **Write these numbers in the correct part of this Venn diagram.**

36
39
90
60
50
40
56
72
70
24
44
54

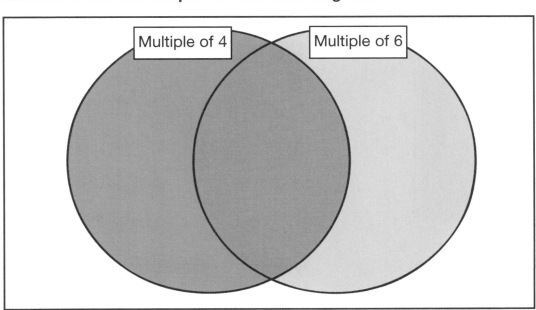

Multiplication

Here are two methods of **multiplying**.

Grid method	Column method

Grid method

47 × 6

	6
40	240
7	42

282

52 × 13

	10	3	
50	500	150	650
2	20	6	26

676

Column method

47 × 6

```
    4 7
×     6
  ‾‾‾‾‾
  2 8 2
    4
```

52 × 13

```
    5 2
×   1 3
  ‾‾‾‾‾
  1 5 6
  5 2 0
  ‾‾‾‾‾
  6 7 6
```

I Use one of the methods to answer these.

a 38 × 6 = ☐

b 54 × 7 = ☐

c 85 × 9 = ☐

d 64 × 8 = ☐

e 219 × 6 = ☐

f 324 × 7 = ☐

g 512 × 4 = ☐

h 284 × 5 = ☐

i 74 × 28 = ☐

j 37 × 54 = ☐

k 63 × 57 = ☐

l 49 × 34 = ☐

Working out

II Calculate the areas of each of these gardens.

a

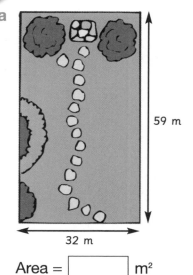

59 m

32 m

Area = ☐ m²

b

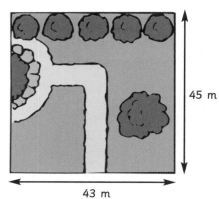

45 m

43 m

Area = ☐ m²

c

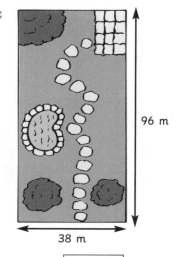

96 m

38 m

Area = ☐ m²

26

Angles

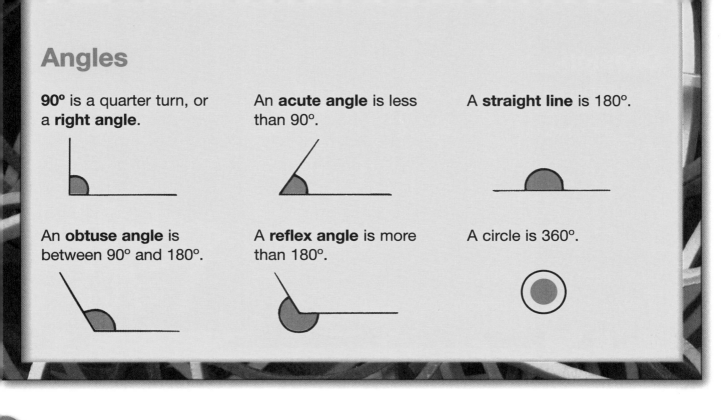

90° is a quarter turn, or a **right angle**.

An **acute angle** is less than 90°.

A **straight line** is 180°.

An **obtuse angle** is between 90° and 180°.

A **reflex angle** is more than 180°.

A circle is 360°.

I Show the angles inside these shapes with coloured dots.

acute angle

obtuse angle

right angle

reflex angle

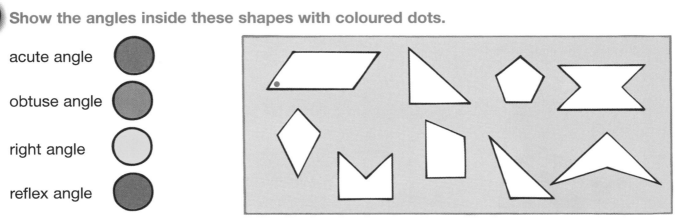

II Write the size of the missing angles.

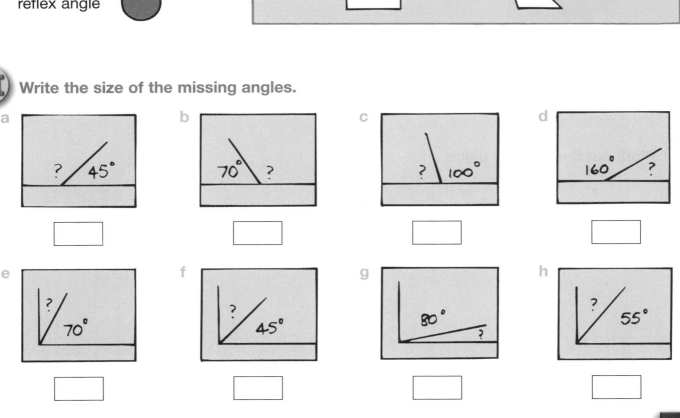

a   ? 45°

b   70° ?

c   ? 100°

d   160° ?

e   ? 70°

f   ? 45°

g   80° ?

h   ? 55°

Division

Here are two methods for **dividing** numbers.   197 ÷ 6

```
      32 remainder 5
6 | 197
   -180
     17
   - 12
      5
```

This is the short method.

```
        32 remainder 5
6 | 19,7
```

Try to make a quick estimate:

197 ÷ 6 is approximately 200 ÷ 5 which is 40.

I **Answer these division problems.**

a

4 | 7 5 6

b

7 | 9 1 4

c

5 | 9 0 7

d

8 | 6 4 5

| 691 |
| 438 |
| 602 |
| 358 |
| 696 |

e Which of the numbers in the box can be divided exactly by 7?

f Which of these numbers has a remainder of 3 when divided by 8?

g Which of these numbers is exactly divisible by 4?

h Which of these numbers has an answer of 73 when divided by 6?

i Which of these numbers has a remainder of 4 when divided by 6?

II **Work out the missing digits.**

a
```
      7 3
6 | 4 ☐ 8
```

d
```
    ☐ 7 r7
9 | 6 1 0
```

g
```
      5 4 r2
7 | 3 8 ☐
```

b
```
      5 4 r3
5 | ☐ 7 3
```

e
```
      8 9 r2
4 | ☐ 5 8
```

h
```
      9 8 r1
☐ | 7 8 5
```

c
```
    ☐ 5 r7
9 | 3 2 2
```

f
```
      5 6 r7
☐ | 5 1 1
```

i
```
      9 3 r4
7 | 6 5 ☐
```

Problems

When you read a **word problem** try to 'picture' the problem.

Try these four steps.

1 Read the problem
What do you need to find out?

2 Sort out the calculation
There may be one or more parts to the question. What calculations are needed?

3 Work out the answer
Will you use a mental or written method?

4 Check back
Read the question again. Have you answered it fully?

I Read these word problems and answer them.

a There are 264 pupils in a school hall.
If 45 more enter, how many pupils will that make? _____

b Simon buys a coat for £54 and trousers for £3.
How much change will he get from £100? _____

c Drinks cost 35p and baps cost 60p. What is the total cost of 4 drinks and 3 baps? _____

d A recipe needs 25 g of butter, 250 g of flour and 75 g of sugar.
What is the total weight of these ingredients? _____

e What is the difference in weight between the heaviest and lightest parcels?

_____

f Which two parcels have a difference of 445 g? _____

II How much change would you get from £20 for each shopping list?

a 1 shampoo
2 soaps
1 face cream

_____

b 3 toothbrushes
1 toothpaste
1 shampoo

_____

c 3 soaps
1 face cream
2 shampoos

_____

29

Time problems

Use a **timeline** to help solve time problems.

Count on from the start time to the finish in easy steps.

A TV programme starts at 2.45p.m. and finishes at 4.18p.m.

How long is it on for?

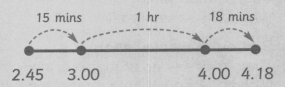

15 mins   1 hr   18 mins

2.45   3.00   4.00 4.18

Total time 1 hr 33 mins.

I Complete this TV recording grid.

Programme	Start	Finish	Total time
Music Box	09:40	10:22	_____
Film: *Bandanna Kid*	11:55	13:08	_____
Visit the Arctic	14:27	15:10	_____
The Big Match	16:05	17:42	_____
Comedy Classics	19:21	20:40	_____
You're on Show	21:15	23:09	_____

II Tick the most appropriate answer.

a Years in a millennium:

100 ☐   1000 ☐   10 000 ☐

b Years in a decade:

10 ☐   100 ☐   1000 ☐

c Years in a century:

10 ☐   100 ☐   1000 ☐

d To roast a chicken:

10 hours ☐   5 minutes ☐   2 hours ☐

e To walk a kilometre:

15 mins ☐   45 seconds ☐   2 hours ☐

f To run 100 metres:

20 seconds ☐   2 minutes ☐   20 minutes ☐

Data

The **mode** is the number which occurs most often.

The **range** is the difference between the highest and lowest numbers.

Mode = 7 (it occurs most often)

Range = 5 (it is 9 − 4)

This table shows the shoe sizes of a group of children.

Name	Shoe size
Alex	5
Robin	4
Ashley	$3\frac{1}{2}$
Kelly	5
Pat	3
Kim	$4\frac{1}{2}$
Taylor	5
Sandy	5
Sam	4
Jo	3

a What is the mode?

_____

b What is the range?

_____

c Who has smaller feet than Sam?

_____

d Who has larger feet than Kim?

_____

e Who takes size 3.5 shoes?

_____

This bar chart shows the minutes of rainfall each day for a week.

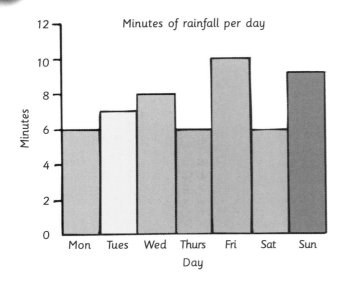

a What is the mode? _____

b What is the range? _____

c Which was the
wettest day? _____

d Which days were
wetter than
Wednesday? _____

e How many minutes of rain fell during the
whole week?

_____

ANSWERS

Page 2
I   a 32 050
    b 480 000
    c 200 512
    d 3076
    e 847 000
    f twenty-nine thousand and fifty
    g four hundred and fifteen thousand
    h one hundred and five thousand, two hundred and sixty-nine

II a 74, 305, 200, 3200, 28 000, 90 000, 48 520
    b 6, 14, 675, 2250, 4800, 25 000, 415 000
    c 8, 17, 141, 6000, 14 000, 29 000, 345 000

Page 3
I   a 37, 73, 82
    b 45, 39, 21
    c −5, 4, 10
    d 14, −1, −11
    e −13, −21, −25
    f −6, −16, −36
    g −30, 3, 36
    h −3, −13, −33, −43

II a −12   c −4
    b −8   d −20

Page 4
I   a 0.1   d 0.94   g 15.73
    b 0.4   e 15.3   h 15.89
    c 0.68   f 15.48

II $0.2 \rightarrow \frac{1}{5}$ $0.3 \rightarrow \frac{3}{10}$
    $0.5 \rightarrow \frac{1}{2}$ $0.8 \rightarrow \frac{4}{5}$
    $0.25 \rightarrow \frac{1}{4}$ $0.75 \rightarrow \frac{3}{4}$

Page 5
I   a 15, 15, 12, 14, 18, 11, 13, 16, 13, 16
    b 6, 6, 4, 8, 7, 7, 9, 9, 4, 8
    c 35, 81, 40, 24, 49, 54, 21, 32, 45, 64
    d 8, 5, 7, 6, 7, 3, 4, 8, 9, 9

II a 39   e 60   i 39
    b 12   f 30   j 14
    c 15   g 49   k 30
    d 19   h 80   l 16
    HANDKERCHIEF

Page 6
I   a red   d red   g blue
    b blue   e blue   h yellow
    c yellow   f red   i yellow

II
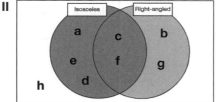

Page 7
I   a 1.82 m, 1.79 m, 1.71 m, 1.7 m, 1.65 m, 1.62 m
    b 87.3 kg, 87.1 kg, 80.2 kg, 79.8 kg, 74.3 kg, 70.6 kg

II a 5.95 > 5.2 > 0.53 < 0.8 < 8.65 > 8.56
    b 21.9 > 20.8 > 20.15 > 2.92 > 2.89 < 2.9

Page 8
I   a 07:30   g 9.30 am
    b 21:00   h 3.00 pm
    c 10:15   i 8.15 pm
    d 16:45   j 1.40 pm
    e 02:10   k 10.55 am
    f 23:50   l 10.20 pm

II a 33 minutes
    b 11:55 from Gradbury
    c 57 minutes
    d 21 minutes

Page 9
I   a $\frac{8}{10} = \frac{4}{5}$ f 9
    b $\frac{4}{12} = \frac{1}{3}$ g 5
    c $\frac{6}{8} = \frac{3}{4}$ h 5
    d $\frac{9}{15} = \frac{3}{5}$ i 18
    e 2   j 4

II a $\frac{1}{10}, \frac{2}{10}, \frac{1}{4}, \frac{1}{2}, \frac{3}{5}, \frac{2}{3}, \frac{3}{4}, \frac{9}{10}$

Page 10
I   a 3500 m   e 25 cm   i 475 cm
    b 4 cm   f 6.5 km   j 6.5 cm
    c 1.5 m   g 220 mm
    d 80 mm   h 18000 m

II a 1.1 kg   c 0.6 kg   e 1.8 kg
    b 3.6 kg   d 2.3 kg   f 2.9 kg

Page 11
I   a 54 and 86   d 229
    b 540   e 124 and 86
    c 154   f 419

II a 8262   e £46.44
    b 11923   f £136.05
    c 6063   g £48.75
    d 9025   h £66.40

Page 12
I   a perimeter 30 cm, area 36 cm^2
    b perimeter 48 cm, area 135 cm^2
    c perimeter 34 cm, area 56 cm^2
    d perimeter 24 cm, area 27 cm^2

II a 81 cm^2
    b 38 cm, 22 cm or 18 cm
    c 32 cm

Page 13
I   a pyramid   e pyramid
    b prism   f prism
    c prism   g pyramid
    d prism   h pyramid

II

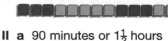

Page 14
I

II a 90 minutes or $1\frac{1}{2}$ hours
    b $1\frac{1}{2}$ teaspoons
    c $1\frac{1}{2}$ lemons
    d 4 plums
    e 100 g sultanas

Page 15
I   a 183   d 688   g 252
    b 77   e 968   h 1387
    c 369   f 173

II These are possible answers
    a 9876 − 2345 = 7531
    b 6234 − 5987 = 247
    c 4965 − 2873 = 2092

Page 16
I   a 9, 100, 36, 4
    b 8×8, 4×4, 5×5, 9×9, 1×1, 7×7
    c 25, 81, 4, 49, 1, 64, 100, 36

II a 8 cm   c 9 cm   e 5 cm
    b 10 cm   d 6 cm

Page 17
I   a 1, 2, 3, 4, 6, 12
    b 1, 2, 4, 5, 10, 20
    c 1, 5, 25
    d 1, 2, 4, 8, 16, 32
    e 1, 2, 4, 5, 8, 10, 20, 40
    f 1, 5, 11, 55
    g (1, 18) (2, 9) (3, 6)
    h (1, 24) (2, 12) (3, 8) (4, 6)
    i (1, 42) (2, 21) (3, 14) (6, 7)
    j (1, 30) (2, 15) (3, 10) (5, 6)
    k (1, 60) (2, 30) (3, 20) (4, 15) (5, 12) (6, 10)
    l (1, 28) (2, 14) (4, 7)

II a 8   e 9 and 12
    b 5   f 5 and 12
    c 9   g True
    d 8 and 5